TALES
OF
nanabozho

TALES
OF
nanabozho

DOROTHY M. REID
ILLUSTRATED BY DONALD GRANT

new york
HENRY Z. WALCK INC.
1963

© Oxford University Press 1963

LIBRARY OF CONGRESS CATALOG CARD NUMBER:
63-19447

PRINTED IN CANADA BY
THE BRYANT PRESS LIMITED

This book belongs to many people,
but I wish to extend my affectionate gratitude
above all to these four:

JACK REID
builder of homes in Nanabozho's forest,
who encouraged me to write it;

PETER MUTCHLER
who coerced (bullied?) me
into finishing it;

WILLIAM TOYE
&
JOY SALMON
of the Oxford University Press,
who edited it.

contents

CONTENTS

preface

If you should visit the Canadian Lakehead and look out
across the blue waters of Lake Superior, you would
see a long low rocky promontory that looks rather like
a man lying asleep, with his hands folded on his chest
and his face turned towards the sky.

The Ojibwa or Chippewa Indians (both names
derive from the word *Otchibway*, "people whose
moccasins have puckered seams") believed that this
Sleeping Giant was once Nanabozho, a great creator-
magician, and they delighted in telling stories about
him. He was bigger, wiser, and stronger than they, but
had many of the ways of men. He was a great trickster,
and the stories of his trickery and of the foolish mistakes
he sometimes made appealed to the Indians' sense of
humour—the story-tellers never tired of inventing tales

of his exploits. They were careful in summer not to tell
any stories that might offend the spirits whose listening
ears were all about them; only in the winter was it safe to
tell these, for then the forest was locked in sleep.

Because the Indians of North America had no
written language, their stories were not set down on
paper until white men travelling among the tribes
recorded them in their journals. (Had they not done so,
some of these stories might be lost by this time, for
the Indian people have turned away from the old
patterns of living.) Many of the Ojibwa tales were
collected by Henry R. Schoolcraft, a geologist employed
by the United States government. The American poet
Longfellow drew the idea for his poem, *The Song of
Hiawatha*, from Schoolcraft's writings, but he called
the great creator-magician by an Iroquois name.

In retelling the stories for this book I have drawn on
many sources and used incidents from the mythology
both of the Ojibwa and of other tribes in the Algonkian
language-group to which the Ojibwa belong. But I have
tried to make my own versions true to the spirit of the
original material, and above all to the qualities of
humour, adventure, and fantasy in which it is so rich.

pronunciation guide

TO SOME OF THE INDIAN WORDS

ADJIDAUMO	Ah-CHEE-tah-MO
ANIMIKIE	Ah-nee-MEH-kee
ATATHARHO	AH-tah-tar-ho
GITCHE MANITOU	KET-chee-MAN-ee-too
KAKABEKA	Kah-KAH-pee-kah (now pronounced Kah-kah-BEH-kah)
KAKAPIKANK	Kah-KAH-pee-kank
KAMINISTIQUIA	Kah-mah-NIS-tih-kwa
KAYOSHK	Kah-YAHSK
KINISHTINO	KEE-nish-tih-nuh

KINNI-KINNICK	KI-nee KI-nick
KOSH-KO-E-WA-SOO	KOSH-koh-ee-WAY-soo
MANATOANO	MAN-ee-too-wah-nah
NADOUESSIOUX	NAH-too-WAY-soo
NANABOZHO	Nah-nah-boh-ZHO
NAHPOOTIE	Nah-POO-tee
NOKOMIS	NOH-koh-miss
OBEKONG	OH-pa-kunk
OJIBWA	Oh-JIB-way
ONGUIAAHRA	Oon-kwi-AH-rah
PAUWATING	PAH-wee-tink
SHOGONOS	SHAH-ka-nahsh
SHUNIAH	SHOO-nah-yah
SOQUAATUM	SKWAH-tum
TIKINAGAN	TEH-kee-NAH-kan
WABOJEEG	WAH-poo-jik
WAUBENO	Wah-BEE-noh
WINDIGO	WIN-tee-koh

THE
COMING
OF
nanabozho

Know then that when the world was new the Ojibwa
had much to learn. Observing their difficulties, Gitche
Manitou, *the Great Spirit, took pity on them and in his
wisdom sent them a teacher.*

*In those far-off times a wise old woman lived among
the people. Her name was Nokomis and she was a
daughter of the moon. Indeed she had once lived upon
the moon with her husband. But a jealous woman had
pitched her into the centre of a lake and she had fallen
through to the earth. There she gave birth to a daughter
and named her Wenonah.*

*The girl grew tall, and skilled in the ways of the
forest. The fame of her beauty and gentleness spread far
among the tribes, and many braves came to Nokomis,
each seeking her daughter for his bride. But Nokomis*

*did not want to part with her only child, and she refused
all who came, saying that Wenonah was still too young
to leave her home.*

*One day the maiden was walking alone in the forest.
Suddenly the West Wind swept down upon her, bending
the trees out of his way and roaring with anger. He
seized the terrified girl and carried her to his lodge in the
Mountains of the West. There she dwelt among the cold
high peaks. She was lonely when the West Wind was
away, but when he was at home she feared his rough
ways and the boisterousness of his sons, the winds of the
North, South, and East. She yearned for her home in the
forest and for her mother.*

*Nokomis sought Wenonah far and near, calling her
name longingly through the forest. At last the Eagle took
pity on the old woman and told her that the West Wind
had carried Wenonah away. Nokomis knew that she
could not prevail against so strong an adversary, and she
resigned herself to spending the rest of her life alone.*

*One evening as Nokomis was gazing far to the west-
ward, she heard a low voice calling her name. At first she
thought it was only a trick of her imagination; then she
saw her daughter approaching and hurried to meet her.
Wenonah was so exhausted from her long journey and
her many hardships that she could scarcely walk. In a
faltering voice she told her mother how the West Wind
had grown weary of her grief-stricken face and had*

driven her out of his lodge.

Shortly after Wenonah returned, she gave birth to two sons. Then, worn out by all her hardships, the gentle girl departed to the Land of Spirits, taking one of her sons with her.

The grieving old woman wrapped the living child in soft grass and placed over him a large wooden bowl to protect him from harm. She buried her daughter and the other child, then sank to the ground. "Wahwonowin!"* she moaned, rocking to and fro. "My daughter is dead!"

For many days she sat lamenting, and she too might have died of grief had not a rustling from beneath the great wooden bowl caught her attention. Only then did she remember the baby she had placed there.

Nokomis hurried to pick up the bowl. Great was her astonishment when she found a small white rabbit. Already the Great Trickster had begun his magic. Weary of waiting for his grandmother to bring him food, he had changed himself into a rabbit so that he could eat the grass around him and not starve.

Nokomis was filled with remorse. She picked the animal up and caressed it, calling it her Nanabozho, her rabbit.

Nanabozho grew rapidly. Being the son of the West Wind and the great-grandson of the Moon, he was more than human and could change himself into many marvellous things—a bear, a tree, a snake, sometimes even a

*A cry of mourning for the dead.

rock to trip his enemies. But his favourite shape was that of a strong young brave. When he walked, the earth trembled, and the sound travelled down to the dwelling places of the evil spirits. Hearing it, they knew that a great manitou* *had been born on the earth, and that they must destroy him lest he conquer them. Nanabozho's life on earth was to be a long war against these evil spirits.*

Nanabozho had many adventures. He often performed great deeds for the Ojibwa people. Many were the stories told about him, and wherever you look in the woods and lakes, there is something to remind you of Nanabozho. The marks on the trunks of the white birch trees, the flying V of the wild geese winging through the sky, even the great rocks that dot the landscape—all are part of his work. The earth itself was remade by him following the great flood.

When at last he lay down to take his long sleep on Thunder Cape, out in Lake Superior, he had left many marks on the things of this world.

*Spirit.

nanabozho
AND
THE
WILD
GEESE

Nanabozho lived with his grandmother in a small *wig-wam* in the forest. He could swim better and run faster than any of the other boys, and he excelled them too in pranks. He loved to swim under water and jerk the fishermen's lines; he delighted in springing the women's rabbit snares.

One day, as he was wandering through the woods looking for mischief, he came to the shore of a small lake. He saw some bright red berries in the lake and tried to pick them, but all he got was a handful of chilling water that slipped through his fingers.

"I *will* have some," he shouted impatiently and

jumped into the lake. He splashed about but could find no berries. Then he glanced upward and caught sight of the fruit hanging from a bush on shore. It was their reflection he had seen. Feeling very foolish, he stamped out of the water.

While he was munching the berries he heard a great tumult of wings over his head. He looked up and saw a flock of geese. They were weary after their journey from the North where they had spent the summer, and were wheeling overhead preparing to land on the lake. Nanabozho hurried in the direction of their flight and saw the birds come to rest on the water with a great flurry and folding of wings. Now he would have a great feast.

But first he had to contrive a scheme to capture as many as possible, for if he dashed in among them he would catch only one or two. Going quickly but quietly back into the woods, he peeled off strips of cedar bark and made a long rope which he coiled in his hand. Then he slipped cautiously into the water, being careful not to disturb the weary birds. He swam under them and tied their legs together with his cedar rope. At the same time he tied each goose to the next one so that he could pull them all up on shore together.

At first all went well, for Nanabozho was so cunning and swift that the geese did not notice him or know what was happening. But his greed betrayed him. Instead of being content with a few geese, he went on to tie up the

whole flock, and just as he was finishing, he had to come up for air. He made such a loud whoosh when he inhaled that the geese took fright. The first goose to fly up was in the middle of the rope and all the others followed. As they rose from the lake they formed a V because they were tied together, and Nanabozho dangled at one end. He shouted to the birds to stop, but the geese only beat the air more desperately with their strong grey wings. Already he was far above the tree-tops, which looked very sharp and unyielding. Just then the birds flew over a stretch of soft swampy ground. Nanabozho let go of the rope with a shout and landed in a bed of oozing mud.

As for the geese, they continued on their way, still flying in a V because of the rope that joined them together. Wild geese have been flying that way ever since, as you can see if you look up into the autumn sky when they go calling past. Some think there is a note of sadness in their cry, but others believe it is derisive, that they are mocking Nanabozho for failing in his trick.

It was not long before Nanabozho forgot the foolish side of his adventure. All he remembered was that he had flown through the air. He composed a song to celebrate this feat, a song he never tired of singing:

> *Flocks of wild geese up in the sky,*
> *Nanabozho flew as far and as high.*

The people listened respectfully to Nanabozho's

song, but whenever he was out of hearing they sang a different one:

> *High in the autumn sky*
> *Wild geese are calling.*
> *Down from the autumn sky*
> *Nana is falling.*

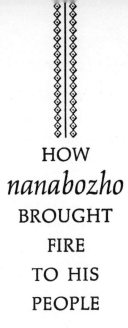

HOW
nanabozho
BROUGHT
FIRE
TO HIS
PEOPLE

In the early days of the world the people had no fire to warm them and to cook their food. Because they saw its destructive power when lightning set the forest ablaze, they were afraid of it.

Once the Coyote went to the underworld and brought back a brand of fire for the tribes. But the people forbade its use and appointed an old warrior-magician to watch over it. Some fearless braves tried to steal it for themselves, but it was always well guarded by the magician and his two fierce daughters.

As Nanabozho himself was young and strong, the lack of fire for heat did not trouble him particularly. His grandmother, however, was growing old and felt the cold severely. In the winter she spent much of the time huddled in her fur robe complaining bitterly.

Nanabozho entered the wigwam one day and, finding her thus, sought to cheer her.

"Come, Noko, come!" he cried. "Get up and go with me into the forest. We will follow the hunting trail of the wolf, and the blood will flow warmly once more through your veins."

Nokomis huddled deeper into her robe and turned her face away from him. "It is well for you to talk," she muttered wearily, "but I am old and slow. Hunting trails are not for me and the bitter wind bites to the marrow of my bones."

The thoughtless Nanabozho was touched with pity. With his own hand he brought her a piece of venison, hoping that food would put new spirit into her. But the raw deer-meat was frozen hard, and Nokomis had great difficulty gnawing it with her poor old teeth. As he watched her, Nanabozho resolved that he would steal some fire for her comfort before another winter came.

The next year, in the moon of wild rice,* he set out for the region where the old warrior-magician lived. Arriving some distance from the lodge where the fire was jealously guarded, he hid his dug-out canoe in the willows. Then, changing himself into a small white hare, he jumped into the water in order to appear wet and

*September.

bedraggled, for he was sure that this would arouse the pity of the magician's daughters.

As soon as he approached the lodge one of the girls saw him, picked him up, and carried him inside, placing him near the burning brand to warm and dry him. Then she returned to her work.

Watching his opportunity, Nanabozho hopped a little closer to the fire. He had forgotten that when he moved he made the earth tremble, and this violent tremor wakened the old magician who had been sleeping on a heap of furs in a corner of the lodge.

"What was that noise?" the old man growled. "What have you foolish women been doing while I slept?"

The girls protested that they had done nothing wrong, that they did not know what had caused the sound. They never thought of blaming the poor little half-drowned hare.

Then the old magician caught sight of the hare. His suspicions were aroused and he got up to have a better look at him. But the small trembling animal seemed so powerless that the old man went back to sleep, muttering about the foolishness of women.

Huddling close to the fire, Nanabozho waited until he heard the old man snoring and until the girls were busy at the side of the lodge farthest from the door. Then, at exactly the right moment, he changed himself back into a fleet-footed Indian brave, seized the brand,

dashed from the lodge, and ran towards the place in the willows where he had left his canoe.

But he had wakened the old magician who instantly saw what had happened and sent the girls in pursuit. Their father's shouts spurred them on, for they knew they would be cruelly punished if they lost the sacred fire.

Nanabozho sped swiftly down the trail, quite confident that he could easily out-run two girls. But when he glanced over his shoulder, he was dismayed to see that they were gaining on him. He doubled his speed, but the girls, by means of magic, ran faster still.

"Come back, you trickster!" one of them yelled. "Give us back our fire!"

By this time Nanabozho had reached his canoe. Behind him was a large meadow of dried grass. "Here is your fire!" he yelled, and plunged the burning stick into the grass. It ignited and the wind carried the flames and dense smoke back towards the girls and halted their pursuit. They could do nothing but return to the fierce upbraiding of their father.

As Nanabozho watched the blaze he had made, he saw how the broad-leafed trees reflected the colours of the fire in brilliant shades of red and gold and bronze. This so pleased him that he decided to make them look this way every year in the autumn.

Nanabozho fixed the burning brand in one end of

his canoe and set out, paddling swiftly and singing:

> *Great is Nanabozho, mighty he*
> *Who captured fire and set it free.*

He finally reached home, and Nokomis received the gift of fire joyfully, basking in the heat it gave.

The people soon lost their fear and never tired of telling how Nanabozho brought them fire.

nanabozho
INVENTS
KINNI
KINNICK

On a sunny afternoon in the moon of the falling leaf,* as Nanabozho was taking one of his favourite walks along the shore of a small lake, he began to feel hungry. Out on the water a number of young geese were swimming, and he decided to see if he could trick them into coming in to shore.

"Come, you handsome young creatures!" he called to them. "Come up on the shore and I shall teach you a fine new dance. It will make you the envy of all your brothers." Nanabozho was certain this would appeal to the foolish young geese.

Sure enough, in a few moments they all swam ashore.

Nanabozho had them form a circle. "To do the dance properly," he said, "you must close your eyes and thrust your necks far out while I sing."

*October.

While the birds did this, Nanabozho chanted loudly. At the same time he began to wring their necks one by one.

After a while a gander who had joined the dance opened one eye, saw what Nanabozho was doing, and let out a horrified squawk; the remaining birds took fright and flew away. The gander started to fly away too, but the angry Nanabozho gave him such a mighty kick that ganders have borne the mark of Nanabozho's foot upon their backs ever since.

Nanabozho now prepared to cook the geese he had killed. By this time he had learned to make fire for himself: he patiently twirled a hard pointed stick against a piece of soft cedar until a spark appeared and ignited some finely shredded bark. He built a fire, wrapped the geese in mud, and buried them in the coals to roast, with only their legs sticking out.

The warm sun and the exercise had made Nanabozho very sleepy and he decided to have a nap. He did not want to leave the food unguarded, so he told his back to stay awake and to warn him if anyone approached.

He had not been sleeping long when some mischievous boys from a nearby encampment approached.

"*Onaway!* Wake up!" cried his back. "There are people coming down the trail!"

Nanabozho got up quickly and looked all around but he could see no one. Once more he settled down to rest.

He had been sleeping only a short time when again his back awakened him. This happened several times, and finally Nanabozho became annoyed.

"You great foolish back!" he said. "You are afraid of every leaf that rustles." He struck it a few blows for waking him without cause and went back to sleep.

His back's feelings were hurt, and it said to itself that it would never warn Nanabozho again.

Then the boys, who had been hiding among the willows along the trail, crept closer. They saw the legs sticking out of the ashes and smelled the delicious fragrance of roast goose. They ate all the meat, stuck the legbones back into the ashes, and went away, laughing at the trick they had played on Nanabozho.

When Nanabozho awoke he was very hungry. Eager to begin his feast, he pulled out one leg after another and found nothing but bones. He was furious. He would have to punish his back for not waking him!

First he piled a great deal of wood on the fire to make a fine blaze. Then he turned around and stood close to the flames until his back was scorched. When he stepped away from the fire he was so stiff and sore that he missed his footing and slid painfully down a precipice. The burned skin of his back stuck on the cliff, and since that time a hard brown lichen has grown on the rocks of Canada.

Nanabozho's back was now bleeding badly, so he

wiped his raw skin with willow stems, staining them red. His people have used these red willows ever since to stop the bleeding when they meet with any accident.

Nanabozho gathered some brown lichen and mixed it with the bark of the red willow to make the first *kinni-kinnick*. Some of it fell into the fire and made such a pleasing aroma that it gave Nanabozho an idea.

He shaped a bowl from some clay, leaving a hole in the side, and baked it in the fire until it was hard. Then he inserted a hollow reed in the hole. In this way he made the first pipe.

He packed the *kinni-kinnick* into the bowl and lit it with a coal from the fire. Then he sat down in the shade of a jackpine to smoke a pipeful. He enjoyed it so much that he forgot the soreness of his back, his hunger, and even his anger.

nanabozho
AND
THE
WEST
WIND

Nanabozho was tall now and powerful—taller and stronger than any of his people. He had learned many things from the world about him, and much wisdom from old Nokomis herself. But one question always troubled him. Over and over he said to his grandmother, "Tell me, Noko, why have I no father or mother as other people have?"

His grandmother always refused to answer his questions; she was afraid that he would try to punish his father for being cruel to Wenonah. But the time came when she could keep silent no longer.

She told him of his mother and of his twin brother who had departed to the Land of Spirits, and then said:

"Your father is a mighty chief, none other than the West Wind, and he has three other sons whom he has appointed as the North, South, and East Winds. His lodge is far away in the Mountains of the West, many moons from here. But do not seek him out. Stay here instead and help your people and me."

Nanabozho refused. He bade his grandmother farewell, telling her simply that he was going to pay his father a visit, and set out with giant strides towards the Mountains of the West. He was determined to find his father and to kill him.

In the beginning his journey took him through the familiar forests of spruce and pine threaded by many streams and bright with lakes. Gradually, however, the trees began to thin out and become more scarce, and he found himself on a great prairie, where the land stretched as far as the eye could see. Tall grasses covered the plain, and great herds of buffalo fed on them.

The grasses and scant willows and aspens bent always toward the east before the power of the wind of the West. As Nanabozho realized the strength of his father, his heart filled with pride. Then his mind darkened once again with his vengeful purpose. Had not the West Wind deserted Wenonah and been the cause of her death? Had not his father given power to his older brothers and nothing to him? His rage almost choked him as he came to the low-lying foothills and saw in the distance the mighty mountains and the lodge of his father.

The West Wind had been watching Nanabozho's progress across the land. Now, as the youth strode up to the lodge, the chief spoke to him sternly.

"What brings you to this place?" he asked. "Do you not know that it is forbidden to any but the spirits of the world and my sons? Go quickly, before I strike you down!"

Drawing himself to his full height, Nanabozho spoke up boldly. "Know then that I am Nanabozho, son of Wenonah, and grandson of old Nokomis in whose wigwam I dwell."

Then the West Wind recognized his son and welcomed him.

For many days they sat together talking. Nanabozho pretended to take great pleasure in the company of his father, but all the time he searched for a way to destroy this mighty chief. One evening he said, "What creature or thing do you fear most on the earth? Surely even so powerful a chief is afraid of something."

Reluctantly the West Wind admitted that there was a certain black stone, to be found in only one place, which could cause him injury if he were struck by it.

"And you, my son," asked the West Wind, "is there nothing that you fear?"

The crafty Nanabozho realized that he would have

to pretend to be afraid of something. "If I were to be struck by the bulrush root," he stammered, "I would be badly hurt."

At the first opportunity each stole away. Nanabozho found a large piece of the black rock, and the West Wind found a bulrush root, for he was wary of Nanabozho, though he knew himself to be more powerful than his son.

Later, when they resumed their conversation, Nanabozho asked his father if it was true that the gentle Wenonah had died because of his unkindness and harsh treatment. The West Wind admitted that it was so.

Enraged by this confession, Nanabozho picked up the black rock and struck his father blow after blow. The West Wind struck back with the bulrush root. Across the prairies they stormed, the tall grasses swaying before them, the great buffalo herds parting to make way for them, the prairie birds rising in excited clouds around them. Through the forests the battle continued, and across the lakes, until at last Nanabozho had driven his father back to the edge of the world. All the while huge fragments of the black rock scattered on the ground, broken off by Nanabozho's blows.*

At last the West Wind shouted, "Stop, my son!" and Nanabozho, who was very weary, obeyed. "I know you are angry because of the wrong I did your mother and the power I gave your brothers. The four corners of the

*These rocks form the great Laurentian Shield and can be seen to this very day.

earth have been divided among the four winds, but you still have the power to do much good. Stop this senseless fighting and I will tell you of my plans for you."

Nanabozho's anger was abated and he was content to listen.

"My son," continued the West Wind, "you must return to your people. You have the power and knowledge to help them greatly. Go and do good, and when your task is finished I will provide a place for you with your brother the North Wind."

Nanabozho was satisfied and returned to his own country. During the long winter months he often sat in his wigwam and thought of the things his father had told him and of the fame he had been promised.

nanabozho
AND
THE
PARTRIDGE

One brilliant spring morning Nanabozho set out on a walk. The ice had melted from the lake and the bare branches of the trees were showing small green buds. Nanabozho had eaten well that morning of a fine catch of trout, and he was in high good humour. The sights and smells and sounds of the forest made him think of the good days of summer ahead.

Suddenly he heard the slow hesitant beat of a distant drum, which gradually quickened until at last the beats merged into a long unbroken roll that carried far into the forest. As Nanabozho continued on his way the sound increased. Entering a small clearing in the woods, he was astonished to find that the loud drumming which had filled the forest was caused by a handsome grey-brown bird who was standing erect on a log and beating the air rapidly with his wings. His plumage was the colour of dead autumn leaves and he had a black-barred tail and tufts of broad black feathers on each side of his neck. As he drummed, his tail was spread in a fan, and the feathers on his neck stood out like a ruff. It was none other than the Partridge.

Nanabozho admired him silently for a moment before he spoke.

"What is your name, noisy one?" he asked finally, in a voice that could be heard even above the noise the bird was making.

The Partridge was alarmed by the sight of the Mighty One towering over him. He tried to appear unafraid, but his feathers smoothed out and his handsome ruff flattened down. Indeed, by the time he found voice to answer, the Partridge had shrunk to less than half the size he had been when he displayed himself on the log.

"I am *Kosh-ko-e-wa-soo*, 'He-who-startles'," he answered timidly.

Nanabozho flung back his head and roared with laughter. When he recovered his breath he shook his head at the Partridge and said, "You could never startle me, you insignificant creature! I will name you Fool Hen. Be glad that I have fed well or I would be tempted to have you for my breakfast. Now be off with you before I change my mind."

The Partridge was deeply offended. He did not dare

to argue with the Mighty One, but even as he fluttered and ran through the brush he was planning how best to convince Nanabozho that he deserved the name *Kosh-ko-e-wa-soo,* and not the insulting Fool Hen.

Nanabozho continued his journey. His path took him along the shore of the lake where the great cedars leaned far out over the blue water. As he climbed over the small boulders beside the lake he began a happy chant, startling the small creatures near and far.

After a time he came to a rocky point that was dangerous and difficult to cross. Setting his moccasined feet firmly in the crevices of the rock, he started to climb. Just as he arrived at the most treacherous place, the Partridge, who all this time had been travelling quietly in a path parallel to Nanabozho's, saw his opportunity. With a great whirring of wings he suddenly flew up almost under the Big Man's feet. Nanabozho let out a shout, sprang quickly aside, missed his footing, and fell with a tremendous splash into the lake. The Partridge hid himself close by, pleased with what he had done.

Nanabozho thrashed around for some moments in the icy water, and when he got out he was very wet and very angry. Sputtering with fury, he started to look about for the Partridge to punish him. The bird lay very still on the ground, knowing that his brown and grey streaked plumage would conceal him. Nanabozho continued searching, muttering to himself. As he moved quickly about in the woods, the sun and the exercise warmed and dried him. Gradually he began to feel better, and his good humour returned.

At last he sat down on the shore, with his back against a cedar tree, and thought over the events of the morning. Then he remembered the Partridge's name and the warning it had contained.

Standing tall among the trees, Nanabozho cupped his hands about his mouth. "O Small One!" he called. "Know that you are indeed *Kosh-ko-e-wa-soo*. You may keep that name. I, Nanabozho, decree it."

His voice rang out like thunder across lake and forest, and the Partridge heard it and was content.

nanabozho
AND
THE
BIRCHES

One autumn day as Nanabozho passed through the forest he noticed some chipmunks hurrying along with their cheek pouches filled with nuts and seeds. He looked overhead and saw that the birds had gathered in flocks; they would soon set out on their long journey to the warm lands of the south, leaving only the faithful winter birds—chickadees and jays and ravens, the grosbeaks and some of the woodpeckers—to keep him company through the winter. The bronze leaves of the birch trees that he saw around him, the brilliant reds of the rock maples, and the sunny gold of the poplars—all would soon lie in a carpet on the ground.

For a moment Nanabozho was touched with melancholy. But he was not depressed for long. The crisp air with its warm autumn scents was good to breathe. Sud-

denly he realized that he was hungry. He looked at all
the busy feasters about him, but their food did not appeal to his huge appetite. Then he noticed a large black
bear coming towards him through the thinning under-
brush. It was slow and lazy, well fattened from feasting
on berries and honey, and almost ready for its long
winter sleep.

Uprooting a small tree, the Big Man patiently waited
until the bear drew near. Then, chanting a song of
apology to the bear (explaining that he, Nanabozho, was
hungry and needed its body for food and its fur for
warmth in the winter days ahead, and begging the
animal's spirit not to be angry), he showered blows on
the animal with the tree-root. The bear was much too
drowsy to protest.

Nanabozho removed the bear's heavy coat and hung
it to dry on a tree, then cut up the meat and roasted it
over a fire. When it was cooked, he cut it up into small
pieces, for he intended to enjoy his feast by eating it
slowly.

As he was about to take his first mouthful he was
startled by a strange sound in some nearby birch trees
whose branches rubbed together as the wind blew.

"Greedy fellow! Greedy fellow!" they seemed to say.
Nanabozho thought they were scolding him for keeping
the feast to himself (a large animal such as a bear was
always shared by his people), and he shouted to the trees

to stop. But the wind continued to blow and the trees to creak, "Greedy fellow! Greedy fellow!"

Nanabozho was now in a rage. Leaving his feast beside the fire, he climbed the nearest birch to the spot where a neighbouring tree pressed against it. He tried to pull them apart, but even his great strength could not make them yield. The gusts of wind that whined about his ears pressed the trees tightly together and, in his struggle to part them, he caught his hand.

While he tried to free himself, he heard a great commotion in the forest below. Looking down through the branches, he saw a number of wolves approaching. The keen-nosed animals had smelled the meat cooking and had come to share in the feast. They were overjoyed to find the meat so nicely prepared for them and proceeded to devour it.

Nanabozho fought desperately to free his hand. He yelled and stormed at the wolves, but they ignored him. "That is our brother, Nanabozho," one of them said, "climbing trees like a boy. Let us pretend not to see him, for he would be embarrassed to be caught in such a pastime." The wolves quickly finished the food, howled their thanks, and continued on their way through the forest, pleased with themselves for taking advantage of the helpless Nanabozho.

At last the Big Man managed to free himself and came down from the tree. Nothing was left of his meal but the bones of the bear. He tore enough boughs off a willow tree to make a great whip. Then he lashed out with all his strength at the birches that had held him prisoner.

Until then the birch had been the most beautiful of trees, with a trunk of pure glossy white, but the whipping left many wounds, and the white birch is scarred to this day. Once again Nanabozho had left his mark upon the world, a mark of anger.

nanabozho
AND
HIS
BROTHER

At last the time came for Nanabozho to leave his grandmother's wigwam and build one of his own. Here he
lived alone, sometimes doing good, sometimes causing
mischief, depending on his mood.

One day his father the West Wind held a council
with Nanabozho's elder brothers, the winds of the
North, South, and East. Together they agreed that it was
not good for Nanabozho to continue to live alone, and
they decided to bring back to the world of the living the
twin brother who had died at birth.

Nanabozho was overjoyed to have the companionship of his brother, and named him Nahpootie, Skilful
Hunter. The brothers lived happily together; Nanabozho did more good deeds and got into less mischief,
and all the people and things of the world were the better
for his good nature. But the *windigoes,** who for so long

*Evil spirits.

had feared Nanabozho, were very angry to learn that another magician had been put among them. Soon they were plotting to destroy Nahpootie.

One day the Otter came to Nanabozho. "Wise One," he said, "do not let your brother Nahpootie travel on the water, for great danger lies there. Today as I was fishing I heard the evil ones beneath the lake plan how they would catch him and pull him down and drown him."

Nanabozho was grateful to the Otter. He patted his sleek head and said, "Because you have done me a kindness, you and your children shall be the happiest of wild creatures. You shall take pleasure in sporting in the water and sliding on the banks of lakes and streams."

Then Nanabozho hastened to warn Nahpootie, who promised to be careful and to avoid travelling on the lakes and rivers.

At first all went well. But one winter evening, as Nahpootie was returning home from a long hunting trip, he found himself on the shore of the lake opposite the wigwam. Deciding that the Otter's warning applied only to the open water and not to the frozen surface of the lake made hard by many frosts, Nahpootie threw caution to the winds and started across. He proceeded smoothly until he was in the middle of the lake; then he heard ominous cracking sounds and saw a split forming in the ice with water seeping through it. Summoning all his speed, he dashed forward; but before he could reach the safety of the shore the gap opened wide and he disappeared beneath the surface of the lake.

The winter passed and Nanabozho waited anxiously for his brother to return. He began searching everywhere. One day, as he was walking beneath some trees, he spied a Kingfisher high in the branches.

"Have you seen my brother, Kingfisher? Even now can you see him returning from his hunting?"

"Never again will you see your brother, O Nanabozho," the Kingfisher shouted mockingly, "for the evil spirits have drowned him in the lake. Soon they will throw his body on the shore, and that will be a feast for me."

Nanabozho was overwhelmed with anger when he heard these words. But he hid his feelings and said mildly, "Come down to me, for I have a fine belt for you to wear. It will make you one of the handsomest of birds, the envy of all."

The Kingfisher, who was a conceited bird, dearly loved to be noticed. He flew down to Nanabozho's side and let the Big Man put the belt around his breast. As Nanabozho tied the ends of the belt, he made a slip knot, planning to pull it tight and strangle the Kingfisher. But the bird was alert and noticed Nanabozho's quickened breathing. Before the knot could be tightened, the Kingfisher darted away and perched high in the branches, preening himself.

The belt can be seen on kingfishers to this day. It reminds them to be wary of men and to refrain from mocking them. Now their angry cry is only heard if they have failed to catch their prey.

Nanabozho did not lose hope for his brother's return and continued to watch for him. Then one night a spirit came to him in a dream and told him that Nahpootie would never be restored to life again; he had gone once more to the Land of Spirits beyond the Great Mountains. Nanabozho was filled with sadness, but the spirit assured him that Nahpootie would wait for him in the faraway land until Nanabozho's work on earth was done.

Nanabozho continued to live alone and to go out among the people, but his mind was filled with thoughts of vengeance.

nanabozho's
REVENGE

For some time after the death of Nahpootie, the King-fisher went about his fishing in a melancholy mood. Though he had escaped from Nanabozho and had obtained a handsome belt into the bargain, he was troubled because the Big Man was angry with him and he pondered how to make peace with Nanabozho.

One day, as he sat high up in a tree, watching for a fish to break the surface of the water, an idea came to him. He gave one of his loudest, noisiest calls, startling the fish and sending them all to the bottom of the lake. But the Kingfisher did not notice, for already he was flying off to seek Nanabozho.

He found the Big Man walking sadly along the shore of the lake where his brother had been drowned.

"O Mighty One," said the Kingfisher, "it was an evil day when I mocked you. Let there be peace between us. It may be that I have knowledge that will help you."

"The whereabouts of the *windigoes* who captured Nahpootie is the only knowledge I desire," replied Nanabozho. "This would be worth the price of peace between us, O Loud-voiced Fisherman."

"Know then that those you seek dwell beneath the lake. Each day, when the sun is high in the heavens, they come out to lie on the sandy shore on the east side of the lake."

The Big Man was grateful to the Kingfisher. Understanding his vanity, he rewarded the bird by ruffling the feathers on his head to form a handsome crest.

Then Nanabozho hastened to the east shore of the lake. He hid his great war-club, changed himself into an old pine stump, and settled down to wait.

He had not been there long when the monsters began to crawl out of the water, all of them beautiful glistening shades of red and green and yellow. One of them, larger than all the rest and pure white in colour, was their prince.

As the monsters stretched and frolicked on the warm sand, the white prince noticed the stump. He was sure it had not been there before, and he wondered if it was an enemy in disguise. One after another his followers wound around the stump and squeezed hard. Twice Nanabozho almost cried out, but each time the monster gave up just as the Big Man was about to reveal himself.

The prince decided that he must have been mistaken

about the tree stump, so he contented himself with basking in the sun. At last the warmth made him sleepy. He dozed off, and the others grouped around him did the same.

Changing himself back into an Indian brave, Nanabozho picked up his great war-club from where it was hidden and, stepping lightly between the sleeping monsters, struck and killed the white prince. Then, uttering a loud shout, he sped away.

There was a dreadful outcry on the beach and the monsters set out to capture and punish the slayer of their prince. Though Nanabozho ran with mile-long strides, the monsters also had magic powers and were soon close on his heels. But just when they were about to capture him, they were forced to return to their natural place— they had travelled as far away from the lake as they dared to go. Using their strongest magic, they sent the waters of the lake rushing after the Big Man to drown him.

Nanabozho was forced to climb a mountain, and when he reached the summit he climbed its tallest tree. He looked down and saw the great flood of water rushing in his direction. Soon it covered the mountain he was on.

"Brother Tree," shouted Nanabozho, "grow taller or the water will drown me." The tree stretched upwards. "Higher yet!" the Big Man called, and the tree obeyed. "Still higher!" came the cry. But the tree could grow no more.

The water rose until it reached the top of the tree. It rose until it touched Nanabozho's chin. Then it stopped.

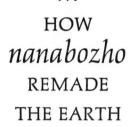

HOW
nanabozho
REMADE
THE EARTH

Nanabozho saw the Eagle flying high above him and cried out, "Great bird, go swiftly and warn my people of their danger! Tell them to get in their canoes so that they may ride safely on the water. Tell them also that I shall return to them as soon as I am able, and stay with them to give them courage and help."

Flying over the flooded country, the Eagle saw that the waters, which had first travelled in the direction of Nanabozho's flight, were slowly spreading in all directions. Because the Ojibwa encampment was built on high ground, the flood had not yet reached it; but the dug-out canoes, which had been beached along the shore of the lake, had all been carried away by the rising water.

The Eagle found the people in the camp preparing their evening meal, unaware of their peril. He gave Nanabozho's message to Nokomis and to the chiefs, and told them of the loss of the canoes. The people were filled with despair when the Eagle told them that there was no time to build new canoes, or even a raft.

Silently Nokomis walked to the water's edge and gazed at the rising moon. Lifting her arms in supplication, she cried out, "Listen, O Moon, to the voice of your daughter Nokomis. Since I came to dwell on earth, I have borne hardships and trials without complaint. Now I ask a favour for my people and for their children. Hold back the waters, I beg you, until we can escape."

The Moon heard the voice of her daughter. She cast her beam in a silver pathway and held back the water so that it could not flood the encampment. (Since that time the Moon has always had power over the great bodies of water on the earth.)

At once the people set to work. The men cut down trees and the boys trimmed off the branches. Then the young women and the girls lashed them together to make a great raft. Nokomis instructed the women to make handholds of cedar rope on the logs. Then she showed the grandmothers how to protect the babies against the weather. She wrapped one of them in doeskin, lined with cat-tail down and laced up the front. Then she padded a thick piece of bark with deerskin and laid the baby on it, with a shelf across the bottom for his feet to rest on and a hoop of wood projecting from the top to protect his face in case the *tikinagan** was upset.

Nokomis showed the mothers how to carry the

*Cradleboard.

cradleboards safely on their backs, with a carrying strap going around their own forehead. In this way their hands would be free to hold onto the raft.

Suddenly the Eagle called out that the Moon's power was waning and that the water was breaking free. The people climbed quickly on the raft, placing the young children in the centre, with the old women to care for them. The mothers sat next, in a circle facing outward, with their babies protected behind their backs. Then came the other women and the young girls sitting shoulder to shoulder. Last of all, in the outer circle, were the men and the older boys, ready for any danger.

As the last man took his place, a great wall of water swept down upon the raft and the people clung to the rope-holds. The raft tipped so steeply that for a moment it seemed as if it might overturn. But the fury of the water was spent, and the raft rode out upon the flood.

The babies looked out with their dark brown eyes at this strange new world of water, or slept, lulled by the swaying motion. Some men fished and shared their catch with the others.

Thus the people waited patiently for Nanabozho to rescue them.

Nanabozho had been swept away from the tree-top and was floating on a great body of water, with no land visible. He saw other creatures swimming desperately about, and realized that he would have to do something to help them.

"Brother Beaver!" he called. "Go down into the water and bring up some earth so that I may make the world anew."

The Beaver obeyed, slapping the water with his tail. (Since then beavers have always slapped the surface of the water as a signal of danger.) Down, down, down he went into the watery depths. Time passed. Just when Nanabozho feared that the animal had been drowned, he reappeared, almost dead but without any earth.

Next Nanabozho and the other animals persuaded the Otter that he should try. He was gone even longer than the Beaver, but he had no more success.

Nanabozho was almost resigned to floating about forever when the Muskrat, who had been swimming nearby, propelled himself swiftly towards the Big Man, using his long tail as a rudder.

"Nanabozho, Nanabozho!" he called. "Let me try to get some earth. I am not as large or as strong as the Beaver or the Otter, but I would like to help you and so gain some measure of fame for myself."

"Very well, you may have your chance. But remember that both the Beaver and the Otter were close to death when they returned, and yet neither was able to reach the bottom."

"No matter what may happen, O Mighty One, be

sure to examine my paws carefully when I return." And the Muskrat disappeared from sight, leaving only an eddy of ripples to mark where he had been.

Everyone waited anxiously. At last, after a day and a night had passed, the Muskrat's body rose to the surface of the water.

Nanabozho pried open the small paws and, under one of the claws, found a tiny lump of mud. He called the Turtle to him and put the mud on its shell. When it was almost dry he began to knead it, turning it over and over. Under his skill the ball of mud grew larger until it became a mountain which he broke up and spread all about, making a raft of mud on the face of the waters.

Nanabozho sent the Bear to trample on the world and smooth it down. But the Bear was too heavy. Water oozed up with every step he took, making the land swampy. If Nanabozho had not called him back, all the earth would have been *muskeg*.

Now the Raven was sent to find Nokomis and the people. When he did not come back, Nanabozho ordered the swift-flying Hawk to find him. The Hawk returned and told Nanabozho that he had seen the Raven feasting on the dead bodies of animals which were lying along the shore.

Nanabozho flew into a rage.

"Never again shall the Raven have anything to eat except what he steals!" the Big Man shouted.

Then he sent the Caribou to inspect the earth. After a long time the animal returned, quite exhausted, and Nanabozho knew that the world was large enough.

"O Mighty One," said the Caribou when he had recovered his breath, "far out on the water I saw Nokomis and the people on a raft."

Nanabozho sent the Moose to fetch them and waited anxiously. At last he saw a speck in the distance. It grew larger and larger until he recognized the raft; it was being pushed by the Moose.

Soon Nokomis and the others thankfully stepped once more upon solid ground.

Nanabozho took the trees of which the raft had been built and used them to create forests on the new earth. The birds that for so long had been flying wearily about came down and settled in the tree tops, and the animals found shelter and rest beneath the branches.

Gitche Manitou was proud of his people who had shown themselves brave and steadfast. His smile broke forth like bright sunshine after a storm. It sparkled on the waters and danced on the leaves of the trees, dappling the ground beneath them.

All the world was warmed by it.

nanabozho
SAVES
NOKOMIS

Nanabozho's enemies, the *windigoes*, were always seeking to annoy and injure him. Once they decided to kill old Nokomis.

Now of all creatures of the earth, Nanabozho loved his grandmother Nokomis the best. It was she who had brought him up from childhood and taught him many things. Though he was now a grown man and no longer lived in her wigwam, she still did what she could to make life easier for him.

In the darkest hours of the night the Evil Ones met to plot. But a Flying Squirrel passed by and heard them mention Nokomis. He listened while the whole plan was unfolded. Then he hurried to tell Nanabozho.

It was now deepest night, and the Big Man was sleeping soundly. The Flying Squirrel bounced noisily on the top of the wigwam. "Nanabozho! Nanabozho!

Wake up!" he called. "There is danger in the forest!" But Nanabozho only turned over and began to snore.

Hours passed and dawn crept into the sky. The Squirrel grew desperate; he would soon have to return to his nest where he would sleep away the day. Through the opening in the top of the wigwam he could see Nanabozho still sleeping peacefully. Suddenly an idea came to him. He found a large pine cone, carried it to the opening, and dropped it on the sleeper's upturned face.

Nanabozho wakened with a start and began to grumble and growl. Looking up, he saw the small bright eyes of the Squirrel peering down at him. He was just about to throw the pine cone back at the Squirrel when the little animal began to speak.

"Do not strike me, Nanabozho!" he said. "I have a warning for you. Great danger threatens old Nokomis."

At these words Nanabozho was wide awake. He listened carefully while the Squirrel told him of the evil ones' plans.

"I know a place where the old woman will be safe," said the little animal. "On the other side of a great waterfall there is a grove of maple trees. It can only be reached by crossing over the falls on a narrow log."

Nanabozho thanked the Squirrel and said, "Surely you are the gentlest and friendliest of all the creatures of the night. May you live in peace and contentment, untroubled by enemies."

Then he gave the little animal some hazel nuts to eat. After the Squirrel had feasted on them, he told Nanabozho how to reach the waterfall, and glided off contentedly to his nest in a poplar tree.

Nanabozho hastened to warn Nokomis and found the old woman about to prepare breakfast. She grumbled when Nanabozho told her that they must leave at once, but she rolled the sheets of birch bark from her wigwam into a bundle, put it on her back, gathered up her sewing tools in a skin bag, and was ready to set out.

After travelling for many hours they came to the place the Flying Squirrel had described—an enormous roaring waterfall that filled the air with spray. They crossed over the falls on the narrow log and Nanabozho began to build a wigwam. He put up a framework of poles, which Nokomis covered with the sheets of birch bark secured with rope to keep them from blowing away. Then Nanabozho set off to waylay the spirits that threatened his grandmother.

The evil ones, however, had their own method of discovering things, and they knew where Nokomis was hidden. In great glee they set out to destroy her while Nanabozho was away. When they reached the falls they stopped short, for on the other side there appeared to be a raging fire. (All this took place in the fall of the year, and what the *windigoes* saw through the mist of the falls were maple leaves aflame with colour.) They consulted each other, decided that Nokomis must have been destroyed in the fire, and went away defeated.

When Nanabozho learned of the part the maple trees had played in protecting his grandmother, he rewarded them by making them especially valuable to men. The next spring he made the sap within the trees grow sweet and flow generously. He cut a gash in the bark and inserted a hollow reed which carried the sap to a birchbark trough. Then he dropped red hot stones into the sap until it boiled and turned to sugar.

Nokomis taught these things to the people. They were grateful to the maple trees for their sweet gift and cherished them, and every spring thereafter was a time of merriment and feasting.

nanabozho
AND
THE
GREAT
STURGEON

One day in spring Nokomis came to Nanabozho and said, "For a long time I have been without oil to put on my head and now my hair is fast falling out for the want of it."

Nanabozho remembered that in a lake nearby dwelt a spine-backed sturgeon—a fine source of oil—who preyed upon swimming animals and fishermen and was so huge that he could swallow even a full-grown moose, antlers and all, without difficulty. He only appeared above the surface at the moment of attack; the rest of the time he skulked about in the depths of the lake.

Nanabozho decided that the only way to destroy the great fish was from within. In some way he must contrive to have the sturgeon swallow him whole; then he could carry out his attack. His grandmother was greatly concerned when she heard what he planned to do, but he said to her, "Do not fear, Nokomis. Go and make me a fishing line of cedar bark." Then he started to construct a birch-bark canoe.

Until this time the Ojibwa had made their boats by hollowing out tree trunks or by lashing logs together with ropes of fibre. The first had been heavy and unwieldy, the second had offered little protection from the storms that sometimes swept the lake. Nanabozho, with his skill, now made a craft that was incredibly light, yet strong and manoeuvrable. He built the framework from the boughs of cedar trees, bending them into the shape he wanted. Then he cut a great sheet of birch bark and spread it on the ground. Laying the skeleton of his boat upon it, he drew the birch bark tightly over the frame and with a bone needle and some *watap** laced the edges. Then he sealed the joints and lacing-holes with hot pine gum. (In this same way his people made their canoes for hundreds of years, and when the white man came to North America he used this craft to explore the country and to carry on the fur trade.)

When his canoe was completed the Big Man stepped into it and set out on his perilous adventure.

He paddled to the centre of the lake, let down a line, and began to chant a loud defiant war song to the Great Sturgeon. He called him many unpleasant names, and

*Prepared roots of spruce trees.

dared him to come up from the depths and do battle with him. Nanabozho's raucous voice, echoing in the deep waters, caused all the fish to dart about and gave the Great Sturgeon a headache.

"Silence that noisemaker!" he shouted to the Trout. "Go and take hold of his fish-line and satisfy him."

When the Trout came to the surface, holding onto the line, Nanabozho was furious.

"Go back to the cowardly Sturgeon and tell him to come up and fight me himself if he is not too frightened," he said to the fish as he freed it from the hook. "Go, for I shall sing my war chant until he does." And he returned the fish to the lake.

Nanabozho then increased the noise he had been making. In desperation the Great Sturgeon rose to the surface himself. Opening his huge mouth, he swallowed the Big Man, canoe and all. Nanabozho bumped his head against a great row of teeth and became unconscious.

When he came to, he found himself inside the stomach of the fish. Though it was pitch dark he could see, for he had eyes like a cat. Soon he realized that he was not alone; the monster had swallowed other creatures that day. There were bears, deer, beavers, foxes—even a red squirrel. Only the Squirrel seemed to have any courage left; the others were quite without hope and expected to die at any minute.

The Big Man called them together. "Listen, my

brothers," he said to the trembling animals, "if we all work together we may still escape."

"Yes, yes," chattered the Squirrel, "that is just what I have been telling them, but no one can think of a plan."

The Squirrel was bouncing up and down as he spoke, and the sight gave Nanabozho an idea.

"We can make it very uncomfortable for the fish if we jump about inside his stomach. I will sing my war chant again for you to dance to."

Filled with new hope, the animals began a frenzied war dance, leaping and shouting and banging on the walls of their prison. The Squirrel leaped as energetically as the others, but he was so small that he was in danger of being trampled. Nanabozho placed him on his shoulder where the valiant little animal shouted encouragement.

The Great Sturgeon became almost frantic with the noise and the turmoil in his stomach. He turned over several times in the water, trying to quiet the creatures who were troubling him. This sent them all rolling topsy-turvy and made them breathless, but as soon as they had recovered, they started up again. And Nanabozho pounded on the fish's great heart with his war club, causing the fish to feel very ill.

"I must get rid of them," the Sturgeon rumbled. "I will throw them out in the centre of the lake where they will all be drowned."

From his place on Nanabozho's shoulder the Squirrel could hear the Sturgeon's voice even above the din. He leaned over and called into Nanabozho's ear, "Pull your canoe across his throat! Hurry! Hurry!"

Just as Nanabozho did this, a great convulsion tumbled everyone towards the fish's throat. But they did not fall out; instead they clung to the canoe which lodged in the passageway.

Nanabozho laughed to see the Squirrel perched on the canoe, chattering busily and flicking his tail in the excitement. "From this day forward," the Big Man said, "you shall be called *Adjidaumo*, 'Tail-in-the-air'."

Nanabozho next attacked the Sturgeon's heart in earnest, and soon the fish was dead. Its body rose to the surface of the water and floated towards the shore; then it scraped against the sand.

While the animals were arguing about how to make their escape, Nanabozho heard a scratching sound. Soon a hole appeared in the fish's belly and light shone through. He peered out and found himself looking at some sea gulls.

"Make the hole larger!" he called.

"It is our brother Nanabozho!" the seagulls cried to one another. "Let us help him escape."

They all began to peck and scratch to make the hole larger, and by and by Nanabozho and the animals were able to step out on land once more.

Nanabozho thanked the gulls. "From this time you shall be called *Kayoshk*, 'Noble-scratchers'," he said, "in token of your kindness to me."

When Nanabozho returned to Nokomis, he found her waiting anxiously. He told her to prepare oil from the fish and to take what she needed for herself. Then he sat down to make up a song to tell of his exploit.

As for the Squirrel, who had scampered off into the woods, he is chattering about his adventure to this day.

nanabozho
AND
ARROWMAKER

Nanabozho had long been dissatisfied with the weapons that he had. A *tomahawk* or even a war club were dangerous to use in his battles with the evil ones, for they meant that he must get close to them in hand-to-hand combat. (Though they did not have the power to kill him, they could do him injury.) And a club was no help to him in his pursuit of swift animals and birds.

But Nanabozho was never at a loss for long. Nokomis had told him about an old man called Arrowmaker who fashioned strange weapons that flew through the sky, and he determined to make some himself. He took straight shoots of dogwood and bound hawk feathers to the shaft with sinew. Then he shaped a piece of ash into a long straight slat, tapered towards the ends. This he carefully greased and hung in his wigwam to dry. When it was ready, he strung it with the neck skin of a snapping turtle.

This fine new weapon made Nanabozho very happy and he proudly showed it to his people. Then one rainy afternoon his grandmother Nokomis came to pay him a visit. She picked up an arrow and studied it; then she said, "Arrowmaker uses sharp heads made of stone for *his* arrows. I will go to him. He will surely give me some."

Nanabozho was secretly delighted, but he always pretended to be skeptical of anything that he had not thought of himself. He merely grunted, and Nokomis set out on the journey.

Though he had seemed to show little interest in her mission, Nanabozho grew impatient waiting. At last, towards the evening of the tenth day, Nokomis returned. The arrowheads she had with her were made from a hard black stone.* The Big Man was delighted with them and spent many happy hours lashing the new heads to his arrows with strips of green bark. As he used them, he grew curious about how the points were made.

"You must fetch me many more of these arrowheads if I am to go on dangerous missions for my people," the Big Man told his grandmother.

Nokomis complained of the weariness in her old bones, but she obediently set out once more for the distant place where Arrowmaker lived. Nanabozho waited

*Flint.

until she had gone a short distance and then quietly
followed her, keeping hidden so that she would not sus-
pect his presence.

When Nokomis entered Arrowmaker's wigwam,
Nanabozho changed himself into a tree so that he could
see everything without being noticed. After a time the
old man appeared and went to a nearby out-cropping of
rock. Nanabozho watched carefully as each arrowhead
took shape.

Just as the old man was finishing, a tall graceful
maiden with gentle eyes emerged from the wigwam.
Nanabozho was struck by her beauty and by the way
she worked so skilfully. Indeed, he almost forgot where
he was, so intent was he on watching the lovely maiden.
Only when Nokomis appeared and bade Arrowmaker
farewell did Nanabozho remember that he had to hasten
back ahead of her.

When Nokomis returned to her grandson and gave
him the arrowheads, he scarcely glanced at them. Instead
he asked for news of her journey, hoping that she would
speak of the maiden he had seen. But the old woman was
weary and cross and said nothing.

Since Nahpootie's death, Nanabozho had been content to live by himself. Now, quite suddenly, he felt
strangely restless and lonely. It was springtime and, as
he wandered through the forest, he was troubled by
something familiar in the whisper of the wind among

the new leaves, in the murmur of the small streams tumbling over the rocks.

One evening, as he sat with his back against a tree watching a bird building a nest, he realized that the winds and streams reminded him of the maiden's voice and of her gentle laughter. He knew then that he would not be content until she came to dwell in his wigwam as his wife.

Nokomis was glad when she heard of Nanabozho's love and told him that the maiden was Arrowmaker's daughter. She made a beautiful doeskin jacket for the girl and decorated it with porcupine quills. Nanabozho made a pipe and prepared a pouchful of *kinni-kinnick* to console the old man for the loss of his daughter. Then they set out on their journey.

Nanabozho chanted happily, and the birds were so astonished that they sang more sweetly than ever. The woods rang with the glorious sound; it reached the ears of Minnehaha, Laughing Water, and she knew that something wonderful was about to befall her.

When the visitors arrived at the wigwam of Arrowmaker, Nanabozho pretended to ignore the gentle maiden who went about her tasks swiftly and well, preparing food for the hungry travellers. After they had eaten, Nokomis presented the jacket to Minnehaha, who showed her delight in such a fine garment. Then Nanabozho gave Arrowmaker the pipe filled with the *kinni-*

kinnick. The old man was puzzled—he did not know what to do with it—so Nanabozho lit it with a splinter from the fire, and soon Arrowmaker was puffing away contentedly.

After a few moments the old man took the stem of the pipe from his mouth and said, "Your *kinni-kinnick* pleases me, but the aroma of its smoke does not compare with that which rises from yonder mountain."

Now Arrowmaker was no fool. He knew why this young man and his grandmother had journeyed so far. He knew also that his daughter found the young man pleasing, though she went about her work with quiet dignity, appearing not even to glance in his direction. But Arrowmaker did not mean to surrender his daughter easily. He was a wise man and could see into the hearts of others. He knew that Nanabozho's life was a difficult one, and he had a great foreboding about the safety of his daughter.

Nanabozho read the old man's thoughts. Rising from his place beside the fire, he said, "Know then that I shall bring you some of the smoke from yonder mountain. In return you shall give me your daughter to be my wife."

Arrowmaker nodded his head in consent, and Nanabozho set out on his new task. He travelled swiftly up the side of the mountain and reached the mouth of a great cave from which the delightfully fragrant smoke was issuing. When he bent down to look in, he saw a giant guarding bags and bales of dry leaves and enjoying a pipeful himself—it was from his pipe that the smoke was rising.

"Keeper of this great treasure," said Nanabozho, "give me a little of it to share with my people."

"This is my *tobacco*," roared the giant, "and none may ever have it! I would burn it all before I would let anyone know its secret."

Nanabozho was angered by such selfishness. He waited until the giant resumed his puffing and, when the mouth of the cave was quite filled with smoke, rushed in, grasped one of the sacks, and dashed away.

Immediately the giant rose in pursuit. The chase took them over the highest mountains where the two of them leapt from peak to peak. At last, as Nanabozho felt himself tiring, he came to a precipice. He stopped abruptly, tripped the giant, and watched him drop head-long over the side into the valley below.

Nanabozho laughed to see the giant hobbling along after his fall, looking like some great awkward insect. He changed him into a grasshopper and, to this day, the saliva of the grasshopper is brown—the colour of nicotine—because of all his smoking when he was a giant in the mountains.

Nanabozho went back to the cave and got the precious *tobacco*, and some seeds so that the people

could plant and cultivate it for their use. He took a sack-
ful to Arrowmaker, and in return the old man allowed
Laughing Water to go with Nanabozho to his own land.

Arrowmaker was sorry to see her leave him, but he
was soon intent on mixing his new *tobacco* with the
kinni-kinnick and, as Nanabozho, Nokomis, and Laughing Water departed, the old man settled back with his
pipe for a good long smoke.

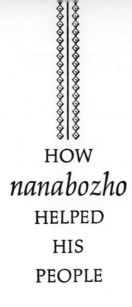

HOW
nanabozho
HELPED
HIS
PEOPLE

In the very early days of the world there had been peace between men and animals, and also among the animals themselves. As time passed, however, the nature of all things changed and man found that he needed the animals' flesh for food and their warm furs to protect him from the chill winds of winter. The animals also began to prey upon one another.

Nevertheless, all might have gone well had the people not grown cruel and careless, killing and injuring the animals needlessly. One day the animals held a great council to discuss what they should do, and finally it was decided that the smallest of the creatures, the flies and the mosquitoes, could best wage this war with man by spreading various illnesses.

Until this time no one had ever fallen sick. The people had died from old age, or been hurt or killed in accidents, but they had never known disease. Now they began to sicken, to suffer fevers and all sorts of discomforts, and many of them died. Because they did not know what caused these illnesses, they were frightened.

Old Nokomis felt sorry for the people, particularly when she saw that even the smallest child was not immune to these attacks. Hastening to her grandson's wigwam, she begged him to help those who were suffering.

Nanabozho had known for some time of the trouble between the animals and man. Indeed, he had spoken to his people and advised them to change their ways before it was too late. Some had listened, but many had continued in their cruel practices. Now Nanabozho suspected that the animals were causing the disease. He knew that he must help his people, who had been punished enough.

As he weighed the matter in his mind, he noticed the Chipmunk scurrying back and forth past the door of his wigwam. Nanabozho knew that if there was any animal still friendly to humans it would be this one who lived near their wigwams.

Nanabozho called out to the Chipmunk, and the friendly little fellow came hurrying over and jumped up on Nanabozho's shoulder.

"Little Brother," said Nanabozho, "there are strange

illnesses among the tribes. I fear that this trouble is sent by the animals to punish my people for their cruelty."

"It is as you have said and it is well known to me," answered the Chipmunk. "At the great council of the animals I alone spoke for men and for their children. The others were so angry that some pounced on me and would have torn me to pieces had I not managed to escape. The marks of their claws are still on my back."

"Then you and your children and your children's children shall wear such stripes forever as a sign of your loyalty to men. But tell me, Little Brother, is there nothing that can be done to end this evil thing?"

"O Mighty One," said the Chipmunk, "the trees and the plants are still friendly to man. Let me go among them and I will see if they have any help to offer." And the Chipmunk scurried away into the forest.

Near sunset on the third day he returned and perched once again on the Big Man's shoulder. He told how the trees and plants had held a great council and had offered many remedies to help man fight disease. The spruces and pines and balsams would give their gums and resins. The slippery elm would give its bark to make a soothing, cooling drink. The ash, the sumach, and the poplar each had a gift to offer, and the plants too —the wintergreen with its bright red berries, the catnip and the boneset, the wild ginger, the gentian, the snake-root, the raspberry, and many others.

Nanabozho was deeply grateful to the Chipmunk and asked him what reward he wanted. The small animal replied, "Only let me remain unmolested near the homes of man." This the Big Man promised.

Nanabozho then asked the Chipmunk to teach Nokomis the use of these new remedies. He himself set out to tell the suffering people that help was at hand, that they should seek out old Nokomis whenever illness troubled them.

As time passed, the people learned the use of the healing drugs. They no longer needed Nokomis's help, though whenever they dug up the root of some precious health-giving plant they would leave a small gift of tobacco for her on the ground.

And the Chipmunk was always welcome about their homes. The stripes that decorated his back were a reminder to the grateful people of the service he had done them.

nanabozho's
JOURNEY

Nanabozho's people depended mainly on hunting and fishing for their food. In the wintertime they lived in scattered bands, some not much larger than one family, in order to follow the game. But when summer came they gathered together in larger groups for companionship and built their wigwams along the shores of lakes or near the banks of rivers so that they could use their canoes. There they had an abundance of wild fruit— blueberries, strawberries, chokeberries, raspberries, and many others. They could harvest the wild rice which grew in the autumn in the shallow water along the lake shores. It was a peaceful life and the people were content.*

Then one day all this changed.

At the time of the flower moon,† when the people had begun to gather together for the summer months to

*At this time Nanabozho and his people lived in the region lying along the north shore of Georgian Bay (Lake Huron) and as far west as the country around what is now Sault Ste Marie, Ontario.

†May.

come, a band of Ottawas arrived from the east. They brought terrifying stories of pale-faced strangers who were travelling up the Great River* in canoes with wings, and who hunted and fought with sticks that barked fire and smoke and instant death.

Nanabozho's face darkened as he listened to the stories, and he rose and departed from the council fire. Walking to the lake shore, he sat down and gazed across the water on which the last glow of sunset was reflected. For many hours he sat there, until at last he fell asleep.

As he slept, the voice of *Gitche Manitou* warned him that he must not harm the *shogonos*,† for they too were children of the Great Spirit. Then Nanabozho dreamed that he went on a long journey into a far country. There he saw a mountain rising above a great stretch of water and near at hand a swift river that entered the lake by three mouths. The voice of the Great Spirit told Nanabozho that he must take his people to this land.

When the Big Man awoke he was weary, as though he had travelled a long way. He sent runners to all the people telling them to assemble in one place and, when they had come together, he spoke to them solemnly and sadly. He warned them that the appearance of these white strangers was an evil-omen, and told them of his dream.

"The time has come to leave this land. Soon the *shogonos* will appear in their winged canoes and take

*The St. Lawrence.
†White men.

our hunting grounds from us. Only by moving far to the north can we escape them."

As the people looked up at him, they saw new strength and wisdom in his face, and they believed him.

While they prepared for the journey, Nanabozho asked the Eagle to carry him to the Great River. There he saw that what the Ottawas had told him was true: strange pale-faced men were camped along the shore of a large island.* For a moment their invasion filled him with anger, and he wondered how he might destroy them. But as he watched, he remembered that they too were children of *Gitche Manitou*, and that he had no right to harm them.

With heavy heart he climbed once more on the Eagle's back. High above the rapids of the Great River they soared, above *Manatoana*, "the garden of *Manitou*", which we call the Thousand Islands. They flew over a vast lake and looked down on *Onguiaahra*—"the thunderer of waters". (White men could not pronounce the Indian name and called it Niagara.) At last they reached the fruitful land Nanabozho knew and loved so well. The people were waiting, many thousands of them, their canoes lying low in the water.

Nanabozho stepped into his own canoe, gave a signal, and set out. The people followed.

North and west they travelled until they came to a place they named *Pauwating*—"the place of the shallow

*Montreal.

cataract".* Then they entered *Gitche Gumee*—"the Big Sea Water".† Here great hills of rock appeared along the shore and rushing rivers flowed into the lake. Many times the people complained of their weariness and wanted to end their journey, but Nanabozho urged them on. Weeks passed, and at last in the distance Nanabozho saw one mountain that stood higher than the rest, commanding the lake and the country round about, and he told his people that this was where they would stay. They looked unhappily at the strange harsh land and yearned for the home they had forsaken to the south, but they were glad that their journey was over at last.

The people made their camp at the foot of the mountain, near the river with three mouths which they called *Kaministiquia*—"the place where there is always plenty of game". There was easy access to good fishing waters, and plenty of fruit and wild rice.

They had already begun to erect the poles for their wigwams when a new danger threatened. The mountain in whose shelter they were camped was the home of *Animikie*, the great Thunderbird, who was indignant to find these strangers in his domain. He circled overhead, shooting bolts of lightning from his eyes and thunderclaps from his wings, and whipping up the waves into a great storm. The sky turned inky black and the people were filled with fear. They begged Nanabozho to lead them away from such a terrifying place.

*Sault Ste Marie.
†Lake Superior.

But Nanabozho knew that this was where they were meant to stay. He started to climb the mountain and made his way upward in spite of the fury of the storm; when he reached the top, he sat down quietly. This increased the Thunderbird's rage and he sent down rain in great torrents. Still the Big Man waited patiently and did not flinch when the Thunderbird launched his blinding lightning flashes. At last the bird realized that nothing he could do would make this man afraid. The clouds vanished, the sun shone once again, and the people returned to their work.

Nanabozho remained on the mountain after the storm had ended and quite forgot the Thunderbird. But the bird had not forgotten Nanabozho. As time passed and the Big Man continued to sit and gaze out across the lake, the bird perched on a giant spruce nearby, watching him intently. Slowly, branch by branch, the bird descended until he was very close to Nanabozho. Then he made a small plaintive sound quite unlike his usual raucous call. Nanabozho looked up and smiled. Immediately the bird flew down and perched on his shoulder, and so they remained for some time.

When Nanabozho came down from the mountain the Thunderbird stayed on the summit. The people soon became accustomed to the sight of him and named his home *Animikie-wekwed* — Thunderbird Mountain.* Though he continued to bring storms, the Thunderbird was now Nanabozho's ally. The two of them found pleasure in each other's company, and whatever the Big Man asked, the Thunderbird would do.

*Mount McKay near Fort William, Ontario.

nanabozho
AND
THE
ROCK
PICTURES

Nanabozho left the Thunderbird to keep watch from the mountain and devoted many days to looking about him at all the beautiful and wonderful things of this new land. He watched the children and the young men at their games of skill. He went with the braves out on the hunting trails, and shared their triumph when their hunting was successful. He saw the joy that followed in the encampment and watched the women preparing the skins, shaping them into garments, and sewing beautiful designs of porcupine quills to them when they were finished.

One day he decided to travel up a nearby river* to its source. Near the mouth of the river, where it flowed into *Gitche Gumee*, were great red rocks from which his

*The Nipigon.

people later learned to make the sacred *calumets** they smoked in their councils. Twice a year they would journey to the river to hold their ceremonial games, exchange their news and stories, and obtain fresh supplies of the rock, which they used only for their sacred pipes.

As Nanabozho paddled, he came upon a solid wall of rock under which the river flowed. He raised his great club and struck the rock one tremendous blow. The rock split into two huge cliffs and the river gushed between, soaking him with its spray. Impatiently he flung off his buckskin robe, useless now that it was wet. There it lay, hardening as it dried until it was like stone. Travellers still point to it and call it Nanabozho's blanket.

Nanabozho's wanderings took him up the *Kaminis-tiquia* to the mighty *Kakapikank*† ("high falls"), where he seemed to hear the spirit voices in the thunder of the waves telling him that his time on earth was growing short. Then, in the dusk, a flying squirrel would glide down and rest upon his shoulder as if to comfort him.

Little by little the thought came to him that there should be some way to record all the things he saw. One day, as he was paddling his great canoe along the shore of *Gitche Gumee*, he noticed the smooth face of the rocks rising from the water, and was struck by an idea. Here would be an excellent place to put drawings of the things of the earth!

*Peace-pipes.
†Kakabeka Falls.

He paddled to shore, beached his canoe, and began looking about for some material to use in his work. He searched for some time before he noticed streaks of red* among the rocks. With a sharp stone he scraped out some of the red pigment, crushed it between two rocks, and turned it into powder; then he fashioned a vessel out of birch bark and placed the powder in it to carry back to the water's edge.

But when he tried to paint on the rocks with the powder, it blew away in the wind.

Nanabozho knew that he must find something that would make the powder stick to the rock face. He reached up and removed some eggs from a nest on the cliff while gulls screamed all about him and beat their wings in indignation. Nanabozho paid no attention but broke open the eggs and mixed them with the red powder to make a sticky paste. He plastered some of this mixture on the rocks and was overjoyed to find it did not blow away.

Nanabozho now got into his canoe with the vessel filled with paint. He paddled close to the steep cliff, then rose to his full height in the canoe and began to make drawings with his fingers on the face of the rock. He drew a young deer, and then a cow moose with her calf; he drew a big old bear that he had seen that morning, and a row of spruce trees to represent the forest.

The Big Man was so delighted with his new skill that

*Iron oxide.

he spent many days painting his designs on the rocks. One sunny afternoon, as he worked on a cliff-face high above the Big Sea Water, an Ojibwa chief named Wabojeeg, White Fisher, came paddling along the shore. Now Wabojeeg was always anxious to teach his people new things, and had already tried to make picture-writings of his own, but he had not been successful. Looking up at the drawings of Nanabozho, he was filled with excitement. He tried vainly to attract Nanabozho's attention, but the Big Man pretended not to notice and continued with his work. Wabojeeg, finding his shouts went unheeded, looked about for some way of getting close to the drawings to study them.

The sheer face of the rock stretched above him and Nanabozho was working at the highest place. Taking his *tomahawk*, Wabojeeg began to cut steps in the face of the cliff. He worked for many hours, chopping a stairway up to where Nanabozho was working. At last he arrived at a spot where he could see the drawings up close. Just then Nanabozho nudged him. He lost his footing and fell headlong into the water.

Wabojeeg despaired, fearing that Nanabozho would complete his work before he could reach him again. But he doggedly began to climb once more.

Nanabozho watched him. He knew that if he was to pass on his new-found knowledge to the people, he would have to teach the secret to someone worthy of it.

Here in this brave and persevering chief was just such a man.

Bending down, Nanabozho spoke to Wabojeeg.

"What is it that you seek, and why do you cut these steps into the rock?" he said.

"Teach me the magic of this great sign language, O Mighty One, that I may tell my people, for it is a great and wise thing."

Nanabozho was pleased with this answer. He set to work again and, as he painted, he explained the secret meanings of the picture-writing to Wabojeeg.

It was the moon of raspberries,* and the day was very warm. Often he had to stop and wipe the sweat from his face with his fingers. Once he bent down to get a drink and was startled to see a terrible face looking up at him from the lake. It had black hair and eyes like his own, but the rest of the face was striped with red.

"*Wah!*" yelled Nanabozho. He grabbed his *toma-hawk* and aimed blow after blow at the face in the water. For a moment it vanished, but when the water settled, it reappeared.

Suddenly Nanabozho noticed that Wabojeeg was shaking with laughter. Then he realized that he had been fighting his reflection—his own face streaked with the paint from his fingers. (Later Nanabozho taught the people how to frighten their enemies in battle with painted faces.)

*July.

Nanabozho showed Wabojeeg where to get the red pigment for his colour and how to mix it into a paste that would cling to the rocks. He also taught him to paint on those rocks that had no lichen, for the lichen would quickly cover and destroy the paintings.

In this way Nanabozho's people learned to depict the things they knew in the world of man, and their imaginings of the Land of Spirits.*

*Their pictures can be seen even today on rocks in Northern Ontario and Minnesota.

nanabozho
AND
THE
RACOON

Nanabozho built his new wigwam at the foot of Thunder Bird Mountain. Not far away lived two blind old men. They had been great hunters in their youth and had provided much food for the tribe in difficult times. Now that they were no longer able to hunt, Nanabozho had built them a wigwam in which to live, and brought them a portion of whatever he caught. Nokomis had made a rope of cedar fibres which she fastened from tree to tree, leading from the old men's wigwam to the edge of the lake. By following this rope, the old men were able to fetch water for their cooking and their other needs. Thus provided for, they lived quite happily together, sharing the work and talking of the great exploits of their youth.

One day the Racoon was walking along the shore when he came upon the old men's rope. Curious, he followed it to their wigwam. He hid in the bushes and watched as one of the men came out, followed the rope down to the water's edge, filled his birch vessel with water, and returned to the wigwam.

As soon as he was gone, the Racoon untied the rope. He fastened the end of it to a tree away from the water's edge. Then he settled down to watch.

Several hours elapsed before the second old man came down to get another vessel of water. He followed the rope as usual, but when he reached the end of it and bent over to dip his vessel, he found only grass and bushes. He groped about but could find no water, and he went away bewildered.

The Racoon, who had been laughing in the bushes, now hurried over and moved the rope back to its original position beside the water's edge.

"Alas!" said the old man when he entered his wigwam with the empty vessel. "The lake has dried up and we have no water for our needs."

"Nonsense!" laughed his companion. "I went down for water this morning and could easily dip the vessel full. You must be mistaken."

"Go and find out for yourself," snapped the first man, very much annoyed.

The second man took the dish and followed the rope to the river. But when he bent down to fill his vessel the water was there just as it had always been. He was quite vexed with his companion—he thought that this had been a trick to make him do more than his share of the work. For the sake of peace, however, he said nothing.

A few days later the two old men boiled some wild rice and added four pieces of venison. When the stew was cooked, they poured it into a wooden bowl. Then they sat down with the bowl between them and each took a piece of meat.

They did not know that the Racoon had entered the wigwam. He came quietly over to the bowl and took the two pieces of meat that were left. Then he calmly started eating them.

One of the men reached into the bowl for his second helping and was surprised to find that there was no meat left.

"You must be very hungry, my brother," he said, "for you have eaten my second piece as well as your own."

"I certainly did not," cried the other. "I have had only one piece. You must have eaten the meat, and now you are trying to hide your greediness by accusing me. Or perhaps you would like me to believe it has disappeared, just as you tried to convince me that the lake had disappeared the other day to save yourself from doing your share of the work."

The Racoon was enjoying the quarrel and, thinking to have more fun, reached up and struck both of them in the face. Each man thought the other had hit him. They sprang up and began to fight, knocking over the bowl and spilling the rest of their dinner. The Racoon quickly ate up all the stew and ran out of the wigwam laughing.

His laughter soon ceased, however, for he met Nanabozho. The Big Man had heard the fighting and had come to seek the cause.

"What do you know of the old men's quarrel?" he asked the Racoon suspiciously.

"Nothing at all," was the answer. "Let me pass."

Instead of answering, Nanabozho picked up the Racoon and carried him back inside the wigwam. The old men told their story and the Racoon, still imprisoned in Nanabozho's grasp, was forced to reveal his trickery.

The angry Nanabozho was determined to put an end to the animal's teasing once and for all.

"You have abused the right to travel freely in the day," he said severely. "Henceforth you shall do your hunting only at night, and you will always need to find water when you hunt, in order to wash your food in it." Then the Big Man wiped charcoal from a burnt stick across the Racoon's face to form a black mask and show him for a thief. On his tail he made eight rings, four for each piece of meat that he had stolen from the blind men.

Since that day all racoons have worn a black mask and rings on their tail. They do their hunting at night, and always wash their food before they eat it.

nanabozho
FIGHTS
PEARL
FEATHER

One day Nanabozho and Laughing Water went to visit Nokomis and found her mourning deeply.

"What is troubling you, Old Woman?" Nanabozho inquired.

"Yesterday your grandfather, Nimishomis, came down from the moon to visit me," Nokomis replied sadly, "and, as he was leaving, he was attacked and killed by the evil Pearl Feather."

Now Pearl Feather was a powerful magician. He was clothed all in *wampum*,* and could withstand any weapon. His dwelling could only be approached through a strait that was guarded by two fire-breathing serpents. Their bodies were made of rock and only their heads could move.

*Strings of beads made from shells sewn together to form a kind of armour.

"I shall avenge my grandfather," said Nanabozho. "My strength will prevail against Pearl Feather."

Nokomis looked up at her grandson, admiring his courage but fearful of his pride. "Before you go on the war-path against this mighty one," she said, "you must first spend some days fasting to engage the help of the spirits."

So Nanabozho fasted and kept vigil in the forest. On the fourth day he was rewarded with a dream in which he learned that he must take with him a supply of oil in addition to his weapons. He loaded his canoe with his bow and many arrows and several vessels full of oil. Then, chanting his war song, he set out.

He travelled swiftly across the water until he came in sight of the strait leading to Pearl Feather's home. On each shore were the serpents. But the passage was barred by tongues of flame that shot out of the serpents' mouths.

Nanabozho stopped at a safe distance. "Greetings!" he called out. "I am merely a friendly traveller. Please turn your heads aside that I may pass."

"Never!" said the serpents. "We know that you are Nanabozho. You cannot deceive us with your lies."

Nanabozho sat in thought for a few minutes, then took his canoe as close to them as he dared. Suddenly he shouted, "Look! Look behind you!" as if to warn them of danger. The serpents both turned their heads and

Nanabozho propelled the canoe between them. Then, taking careful aim, he killed them both so that the passage would henceforth be free to all.

By this time a soft gummy substance in the water had enmeshed his canoe. He rubbed some oil along its sides and it slipped through with ease.

Nanabozho was now very close to the dwelling of Pearl Feather, which was at the base of a cliff. He waited until dawn, then began his attack, shouting, "Surround him! Surround him!" He made so much noise that it seemed as if he had many followers with him.

When Pearl Feather appeared, Nanabozho cried, "It was you who killed my grandfather!" and he began to shoot his arrows.

Pearl Feather broke off great rocks from the cliff and threw them at Nanabozho. (One of these boulders hurtled past Nanabozho and landed on a nearby island.* To this day it is the wonder of white men, for it is unlike all other rock formations on the island.)

All day the battle went on, but Nanabozho's arrows had no effect. Just at sunset, when Nanabozho was growing weary and had only three arrows left, the Woodpecker flew past and called to Nanabozho, "Great Brother, aim for the lock of hair at the crown of his head!"

Nanabozho shot his three arrows in swift succession. Before Pearl Feather could guard himself, the

*Isle Royale.

arrows had struck their mark and he fell dead upon the ground. His evil work in the world was at an end.

Uttering a loud cry of triumph, Nanabozho cut off the magician's lock, that he might show it to Nokomis as a symbol of his victory. Then he rubbed some blood on the Woodpecker's head as a reward for his help. These red tuft feathers have been used by Nanabozho's people ever since to decorate their pipes as a symbol of valour.

nanabozho
FOILS
A
WICKED
BRAVE

One day Laughing Water came to Nanabozho in great excitement.

"Husband," she said, "there is a maiden who needs your help. Her name is Waubeno, and she is threatened by a cruel brave, Obekong, who seeks to carry her off to his wigwam."

"That is none of my affair," replied Nanabozho. "Let her parents or her brothers protect her."

"Her parents are dead and her brothers are too young to help her. She has cared for them unselfishly and everyone admires her for her courage and patience. Now Obekong would take her and leave the children with no one to care for them."

Nanabozho's eyes grew dark with anger. He always

had a soft heart where children were concerned.

Laughing Water continued, "Waubeno is now so frightened that she scarcely dares to venture from the wigwam. She is no longer able to hunt and the children grow hungry and weak."

When Nanabozho arrived at Waubeno's wigwam he found her huddled in a corner with her brothers. She had learned that Obekong was on his way with a dog whip, and that he intended to beat her and carry her off. When Nanabozho heard this, he chuckled. Bidding Waubeno stay well hidden under the fur robes in the corner, and warning the children to show no surprise, he changed himself magically to look like Waubeno.

No sooner had he done this than Obekong came striding up to the wigwam.

"I will teach you the obedience a *squaw* should know!" he yelled. "Come out and get the thrashing you deserve!"

Nanabozho emerged from the wigwam and waited for a moment while Obekong continued with his insults. Then, as the cruel brave lifted his whip to strike, Nanabozho seized him by the hair and threw him to the ground. Wrenching the whip from Obekong's grasp, he began to beat him.

Obekong was astonished at the maiden's strength. "Stop! Stop!" he begged, as he tried to dodge the blows that were raining down on him. "I will not trouble you again."

"Will you stay away from our wigwam and keep out of my way when I go hunting?" said Nanabozho, mimicking the voice of a gentle maiden and continuing to ply the whip.

"Yes, yes!" moaned Obekong. "Never did I dream a girl could be so strong."

Scarcely able to contain his laughter, Nanabozho let Obekong go and watched him slink away. Then the Big Man resumed his own shape. He warned Waubeno not to speak of anything that had happened, bade her farewell, and walked away, quite pleased with what he had done.

But Waubeno and her brothers had one great failing —they simply could not keep a secret. It was not long before everyone knew of Nanabozho's trick. Obekong was furious, but he was afraid to annoy Waubeno again, now that she had such a strong protector.

That autumn, when all the people gathered together for the rice harvest, Waubeno fell in love with a handsome young brave named Soquaatum. They planned to be married the following spring when the boys would be old enough to care for themselves.

With the approach of winter, Soquaatum set out for his own hunting grounds which were some distance away. Obekong saw this as a fine chance to capture Waubeno and take her far away from the help of her family and Nanabozho. He left the encampment secretly, going in the direction Soquaatum had gone. After two days, when fresh snow had covered all the trails, he sent a runner to Waubeno with the message that Soquaatum was badly hurt and was calling for her.

Putting on her warmest garments and strapping on her snowshoes, Waubeno set out immediately in the direction the messenger had shown her. She travelled all night and, just as daylight was breaking, came to a wigwam that she thought must be Soquaatum's. She opened the door-flap; standing inside was Obekong.

Waubeno gasped in horror. Tired though she was, she wheeled around and sped away as fast as her snowshoes would let her. Obekong quickly put *his* snowshoes on and followed her.

Waubeno in her terror lost her way and went plunging through the forest. Behind her she could hear Obekong and she knew that he was gaining on her. "Soquaatum! Soquaatum!" she called in despair. But Soquaatum was far away and could not hear her.

Now it happened that Nanabozho had been hunting in that part of the forest. Suddenly he heard the call "Soquaatum! Soquaatum!" Strong and clear at first, it gradually became hoarse and then a whisper. Soon Waubeno came into sight, still gasping her lover's name, and almost at her heels was Obekong.

Nanabozho knew that he was not near enough to come between them, that he must save Waubeno from afar. Using his magic powers, he turned her into a beau-

tiful blue bird and watched as she soared swiftly out of
danger. To this day the blue-jay makes a sound like
Waubeno's hoarse cry—"Soquaatum! Soquaatum!"

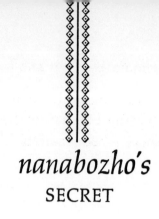

nanabozho's
SECRET

Opposite Thunderbird Mountain was a great cape,* and
Nanabozho would often go there and sit gazing out upon
the Big Sea Water.

One day as he was idly scratching the ground with a
stick, he saw something gleaming in the rock. It was a
shiny vein of *shuniah*!†

Nanabozho knew that the *shogonos* were very eager
for silver, and would brave any dangers to get the shin-
ing stuff. He realized that the secret must be kept at all
costs, for he had become convinced that the hunting
grounds in which he and his people now lived were the
last that would be available to them. Far to the west were
the Assiniboine ("people who cook with stones"); to the
southwest were the warlike Dakotas, whom his people
called the Nadouessioux ("adders"); to the north were
the Kinishtino (Cree). If the *shogonos* came, his people
would have nowhere to go.

*Thunder Cape opposite the twin cities of Port Arthur and Fort William.
†Silver.

For many days Nanabozho pondered. At last he decided to take the strongest and wisest chiefs into his confidence. Gathering them together, he made them swear that they would not reveal the secret of the *shuniah* to anyone. Then he had them make great shovels, and together they dug up all the *shuniah* and stored it on a tiny island less than a mile off the cape. When they had moved it all, they sealed up the entrance to the hiding place.

"Now," thought Nanabozho, "the secret will be safe forever."

But even the wisest of men do foolish things at times.

One of the chiefs had admired the silver so much that he wished to use it to adorn his weapons and clothes. He hid a little of it away and, when no one was looking, carried it secretly back to his wigwam. There he hammered the silver into thin pieces. His wife used some to ornament their buckskin garments; he himself set the rest into the handles of his knife and *tomahawk*. Then they both strutted proudly about with their fine new clothes and weapons.

Soon afterwards the dreaded Nadouessioux went out on the warpath against the Ojibwa. The Sioux were badly beaten and, as they were retreating, one of the braves saw something glittering in the sun beside a fallen Ojibwa. It was a *tomahawk*. He picked it up and saw that the handle was decorated with silver. Coveting more of the shiny metal for himself, he hid until the Ojibwa departed. Then he followed them back to their encampment.

The young Sioux, whose name was Atatharho, crawled into a hollow log and hid there for two days, cramped and hungry. Finally he heard one word he recognized—"*shuniah*".

Nanabozho was speaking to his chiefs. "O my people," he said, "when I found the beautiful metal I knew that it meant danger for us all. I therefore counselled you to keep its presence here a secret. Now, through the greed and vanity of one man, the secret may be known to our enemy the Nadouessioux."

There was a long pause.

"If the *shogonos* learn of the little island with its mountain of *shuniah*," Nanabozho went on, "they will not rest until they find it, and once more we will be driven from our hunting grounds."

The chiefs swore to keep the secret forever.

Atatharho had not understood all that was said, but the words "*shogonos*" and "*shuniah*" were enough. He knew now that the Ojibwa feared the coming of the white men, and he rejoiced in his heart. If the Ojibwa were driven out, then the Sioux in their turn could destroy the white men and have the Ojibwa hunting grounds for themselves.

When darkness fell, Atatharho crept out of the log,

ran to the shore of *Gitche Gumee* where he found an
Ojibwa canoe, and set off in search of white men. In
early autumn, near *Pauwating*, he came upon two traders. Silently the Indian studied the white men, the first
he had ever seen, while they watched the Indian suspiciously. Then Atatharho spoke.

"*Shuniah!*" he whispered.

The word startled the white men.

Atatharho knelt down on the ground and with a
stick drew the Big Sea Water, and marked the place
where they were; then he made a river with three

mouths, drew a long cape and a circle—the island of silver—and repeated the word *"shuniah!"* The word was well known to the white men and they began to talk excitedly.

They did not know that they had been seen by a hawk, who was already flying north to warn Nanabozho. When the Big Man learned that the secret was known to the *shogonos,* he was overcome with anger and sorrow. He and the Thunderbird raged up and down the Big Sea Water, making it impossible to hunt in the driving rain and hail. The waters of the lake heaved and tossed in mountainous billows and the women dared not venture out to fish.

Late in the autumn, Nanabozho returned to his wigwam. The fire had gone out and the store of food was exhausted. When Laughing Water came hurrying in a few minutes later, he shouted at her, "Where have you been and why is there no food? You are a lazy useless *squaw!"*

All day Laughing Water had been trying to take her canoe out on the lake to fish, and time after time the storm had driven her back.

"Why should you chide me, husband?" she said. "You have provided no food for many weeks. Your people are hungry—your storms have made hunting and fishing dangerous. You should be ashamed that you care so little for us all."

The rage that had been in Nanabozho's heart for many days exploded once again and he flung his wife out of the wigwam and up on the cliff.

"Ungrateful woman!" he shouted. "My work has been for you and for my people, but since you do not understand this, you shall stay there forever!" And he turned Laughing Water to stone.*

There she remains to this day, peeping out anxiously across the water as if to see whether her husband is coming home.

*As you drive through the Mission Reserve on the outskirts of Fort William, Ontario, you can see for a moment the full-length figure of an Indian woman high up on a cliff. She seems to be looking out across Squaw Bay in Lake Superior and beyond it across Thunder Bay towards the Sleeping Giant.

nanabozho
FALLS
ASLEEP

Winter passed. The snow disappeared from the hills; the icy bondage of the rivers was broken and the water rushed in great cataracts down to the lake. Everywhere soft green foliage appeared, and the early summer flowers. For Nanabozho this was a sad time. Without the companionship of Laughing Water he was alone once more, and his spirit was heavy. But the Ojibwa were glad of the warmth of the sun after the bitter chill of the winter, and went about their fishing and their tasks unmindful of the danger that threatened.

Many miles away the two white men, who had been unable to travel in the stormy autumn and winter, were journeying north and west into the Ojibwa country, impatient to find the great treasure of silver. Their guide, Atatharho, would gladly have stopped for several days to hunt and fish, but he soon discovered that this was

not the white man's way. Many times he wished he had
not told them of the treasure, and he thought of desert-
ing them. But he was too greedy—the hope of some day
winning the Ojibwa hunting grounds for his nation
spurred him on, and the three men continued to paddle
through *Gitche Gumee.*

At last they could see Thunderbird Mountain in the
distance. The day was clear and bright. The sun sparkled
on the water which cascaded like diamonds as their pad-
dles rose and fell.

The flashing of this spray caught the keen eye of
Nanabozho, who was seated on his favourite lookout
point. Forgetting what the Great Spirit had told him, he
and the Thunderbird brought on a terrible storm, the
most dreadful that had ever been seen on the Big Sea
Water. Thunder roared, lightning flashed, great winds
rolled the waters into giant waves, and torrents of rain
and hail beat down upon the storm-tossed craft that
bore the three invaders. The canoe was engulfed.

Only then did Nanabozho remember that he had
been warned not to harm these people. But *Gitche Manitou* was already casting a spell over him, and the Big
Man fell eternally asleep.

The storm at last died away, and the Ojibwa saw
their friend and protector lying upon the cape, his face
turned towards the sky and his arms folded across his
chest. He had been changed to stone, and lay so near the

little island of silver that it seemed as though he were trying to guard it still.

Nanabozho is still sleeping his long sleep, a thing of stone awaiting the time when the Great Spirit will need him once more and bring him back to life. Then he will arise and continue his appointed work for all the people of his land.

epilogue

Time passed and other white men reached the country
of the Ojibwa, some drawn by the fur trade, others by
a desire to explore the new land and find a canoe route
westward. In 1679 Daniel Greysolon, Sieur Dulhut,
built a fur-trading post on the Kaministiquia River,
and began the first permanent white settlement. The
French gave the Ojibwa guns to use against their
enemies the Sioux.

In 1805 the North West Company built Fort
William, which became the annual meeting-place of the
traders (who wintered in the north) and their partners
from Montreal who brought in trade goods and
returned to the east with furs. Sometimes as many as
three thousand men met at Fort William—their ways
observed with fascination by the Indians.

In 1848 a Jesuit Mission was founded to care for the Thunder Bay Indians. Two years later, in a treaty with the chiefs, the government took over all the Ojibwa territory, setting aside reserves on which the Indians were to live.

Twenty years after the Jesuit Mission was established, a party of prospectors looking for copper found rich silver deposits on a tiny island less than a mile off Thunder Cape. This silver mine became one of the richest in the world, producing over three million dollars' worth of the precious metal. But much of the mine was under Lake Superior, and large engines run by coal had to be worked continually, pumping the water out.

In the late fall of 1883 a barge carrying coal to the mine was caught in a snow storm and turned back to seek shelter. The crew deserted, the captain was forced to tie up for the winter, and no coal reached the little island. The great engines stopped. The waters of Lake Superior flooded the mine and it was never reopened.

Nanabozho's *shuniah* was safe once more.

bibliography

BERTRAND, J.P.: *Highway of Destiny*. New York, Vantage Press. 1959.

BURKHOLDER, MABEL: *Before the White Man Came*. Toronto, McClelland and Stewart. 1923.

DEWDNEY, SELWYN *and* KIDD, KENNETH E.: *Indian Rock Paintings of the Great Lakes*. Quetico Foundation Series No. 4. Published for the Quetico Foundation by the University of Toronto Press. 1962.

HODGE, FREDERICK W. (ed.): *Handbook of American Indians North of Mexico*. 2 vols. Bureau of American Ethnology, Bulletin 30. Washington, Government Printing Office. 1907-10.

HOOKE, HILDA MARY: *Thunder in the Mountains*. Toronto, Oxford University Press. 1947.

JENNESS, DIAMOND: *The Indians of Canada*. 5th ed. Bulletin 65; Anthropological Series No.15. Ottawa, National Museum of Canada. 1960.

LEECHMAN, DOUGLAS: *Native Tribes of Canada.*
Toronto, W. J. Gage and Co. Ltd. 1956.

PIPER, W. S.: *The Eagle of Thunder Cape.* New York,
The Knickerbocker Press. 1924.

RADIN, PAUL: *Some Myths and Tales of the Ojibwa of
Southeastern Ontario.* Canada Geological Survey.
Memoir 48; Anthropological Series No. 2.
Ottawa, Government Printing Bureau. 1914.

SCHOOLCRAFT, HENRY R.: *Algic Researches . . . First Series:
Indian Tales and Legends.* 2 vols.
New York, Harper & Bros. 1839.

SYMONS, HARRY: *Ojibway Melody.* Published for
the author by Ambassador Books. 1946.

Thunder Bay Historical Society, Annual Reports.
Fort William. 1909-28.

TUNIS, EDWIN WAY: *Indians.* Cleveland, World
Publishing Company. 1959.

YOUNG, EGERTON R.: *Algonquin Indian Tales.*
Westwood, N.J., Fleming H. Revell Co. 1903.

The author gratefully acknowledges the permission
given by the Fleming H. Revell Co., Westwood, N.J.,
McClelland and Stewart, Limited, Toronto, and
Mrs. H. Symons to use source material from
Algonquin Indian Tales by Egerton R. Young,
Before the White Man Came by Mabel Burkholder,
and *Ojibway Melody* by Harry Symons.